C000264218

Dear Future Me

from you to me®

from you to me®

concept by Peter Coxon

© from you to me ltd 2010

Most people spend more time planning their shopping or their holidays than they do planning their lives . . .

Dear Future Me

from you to me®

This is a gift in which you can write down your thoughts and reflections on life and create a record of how things are and how you would like them to be in the future. You might like to think about what is working well and what you would like to improve. You can also reflect on what kind of life you want to live in the future, what you believe in and want to stand for. In other words you can start to make choices about what kind of person you want to be.

Please answer whichever questions you like. Also, decide if you'd like to keep your writing private or whether you might like to share some of your writing with a trusted friend, mentor or a member of your family.

We hope that this may help your own development and build friendships, strengthen relationships, set resolutions and challenges and resolve problems. Thinking about the questions and writing about your life in your journal should prove to be a valuable experience. Do stick photos or mementos in your journal if you wish.

People say that we all have at least one book in us and this will be one of yours . . . to be treasured for ever.

You so far . . .

Write down some of your earliest memories . . .

What has helped make you who you are right now?

What things and events in your life have most shaped the person you have become?

What have been some of the biggest events and changes in your life so far?

How have you got on managing these events and changes?

School life . . .

Write about some of the highlights of your school life . . .

What did you **like most** about school life?

What did you **like least** about school life?

What sort of **problems** or **challenges**, if any, did you have at school?

Who were your favourite teachers/tutors and why?

Did anyone inspire you and, if so, how?

Which subjects did you most enjoy at school and why?

What were you best at and why do you think that is so?

Your recent past . . .

What have you most enjoyed doing during the last few years?

What have you found most interesting during the last few years?

What have you found some of the most
challenging things you've done this last year or so?

In what way have you most **changed** or **developed** in recent years?

How have you **improved** this last year and how did you do it?

What has given you the greatest sense of satisfaction this last year or so and why?

You today . . .

Try to **describe yourself** as you are today . . .

What are your **greatest strengths** . . . and what areas would you like to **improve**?

What sports, hobbies and/or interests do you most enjoy and why?

Who is your favourite author and what are your favourite books?

What are your favourite games or gadgets?

How would you describe some of your favourite
holidays/trips/weekends?

Write down the words of your favourite song . . .

Write down the words of a favourite poem . . .

In what ways would you say you have been most
lucky in life?

What is most unfair about life?

7 things that make you **most happy** . . .

7 things that make you most sad . . .

Describe how you feel most of the time . . .

. . . and why is that?

7 things that help you sleep...

7 things that keep you awake . . .

How do you usually and how do you best manage conflicts and fallings out with people?

How might you **manage** such **conflicts** **better** in the future?

Your family . . .

How well do you get on with your family?

Which relationships are easy and which are more difficult?

In what ways are you **similar** to and/or **different** from others in your family?

What do you think your mum and/or dad have **most**
appreciated about you?

What do you think has made your mum and/or dad **most worried** about you?

If you have had **problems** at home what have they mostly been about?

What have you most liked about family life?

What do you like most about the different members of your family?

What do you **like doing** now or what would you **like to do** with your family?

Which other members of your family would you like to write about & what would you like to write?

What have your mum and/or dad done that you have appreciated and would have liked them to carry on doing (or do more of)?

What have your mum and/or dad done that you have **not appreciated** and would have liked them to **do less of** (or stop)?

What have your mum and/or dad **not done** that you would have liked them to do?

What advice would you like to give them or what request would you like to make?

If you are or were to become a parent in what way would you like to be like your parent(s)?

In what way would you like to get on better with your family?

What would you most like to **talk about** with a family member and with whom?

What would you like to **ask** a member of your family?

Your friends . . .

Who are your **best friends** and what do you like about them?

How well do you **get on with** your friends?

Which **relationships** are **easy** and which are more **difficult**, and why?

What do you think your friends **most like** about you?

What do you think your friends **like least** about you?

What do you look for in a long lasting friendship?

How would you like to strengthen your relationships with your friends?

What new things would you like to do with any particular friends?

If you have ever been in love, what is it/was it that you love/d about the person?

What did they /do they love about you?

How might being in love change how you behave?

What has being in love taught you about yourself?

Work . . .

What job(s) have you done so far in your life?

Why did you choose them?

What have you **liked best** and **least** about your work?

What sort of work are you **best at**, and why?

What have you learned about **working with** other people?

In what ways do you think you could **improve** how you get along with other people in the workplace?

Reflecting back . . . write a letter to your younger self

Think of yourself at a particular age . . . what were you like then and what tips, guidance or advice would you give, now you know what was coming next?

Dear Younger Me . . .

Your future self . . . the person you want to be

So tell me what is it you plan to do with your wild and precious life?

Mary Oliver, The Summer Day

Will you leave this world a better place than when you arrived? If so, how might you go about this?

We all have a capacity to be a force for good or a force to make things worse. It is our choice.

How do you intend growing, learning and developing?

The 7 people you would **struggle** to live **without**…

What can you do to make these people's lives **richer** and what would you like to do with them?

What sort of **new friends** would you like to make
and why?

How might you **meet** them?

What can you actually do to be an even better friend to others?

What qualities do you want to develop and exhibit?

How would you like to be remembered?

Whatever you can do, or dream you can, begin it. Boldness has genius, power and magic in it.

Goethe

Write down the first things you would grab from your house if it was on fire . . .

Why would you want to save these things?

Write down the 10 things you think you value most in your life . . .

Now estimate how much time you give to each of these priorities . . .

Think about how you can carve out the time and energy these things you value deserve...

things you **wish were true** …

things you'd like to **change in the world** …

7 things you'd like to change about yourself . .

What are you most looking forward to as you get older?

What would you like to do?

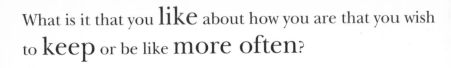

What is it that you **like** about how you are that you wish to **keep** or be like **more often**?

What do you not do that you would **like to do** in the **future**?

Who might be good role models for you with regard to your own growth and development?

How might they or someone else best help you?

What might you need to do **differently** to allow your family and friends to think **more highly** of you?

What would **others see** in you that would **help** you know you are **developing** as you wish to?

What would be your biggest family goal?

Where would you like to live and why?

How fit and healthy do you want to be and why?

What kind of foods do you want to eat and why?

What hobbies, interests, sports or games would you like to be involved with in the future?

What kind of entertainment do you seek or what kind of involvement in the arts do you want to have

How do you like to **have fun**?

What kind of **adventures** would you like to have?

7 books you would like to read . . .

7 paintings or works of art or beauty you would like to see . . .

What artists or types of music would you like to learn more about?

What level of **money** would you like to **earn**?

What would you like to **do with it** when you have it?

What kind of **material possessions** would you like and when would you like to have them?

Why might you **want** these?

Apart from earning money and material possessions, how happy would you be with the person you are and what you have achieved in your life?

What **work** would you most like to do, and why?
What do you need to do to pursue this goal?

What new skills would you like or need to develop

When you **leave** your place of work or study, what would you want your **colleagues** and **friends** to say or think about you?

What **difference** did you make and what **values**, **passions** and **beliefs** did you stand for?

Where would you most like to travel?

.

Think of at least 7 places you'd most like to visit
and why . . .

How will you leave a positive impact on your family, your friends, your community?

How can you make a difference?

What do you want to **achieve before** you retire?

What would you most like to do before you die?

Be creative and make a list of up to 100 important things to do . . .

Continue overleaf . . .

What would you like people to say about you when you die?

Go confidently in the directions of your dreams! Live the life you've imagined.

Henry Thoreau

We have time to do anything but not everything . . . you have to decide your priorities. Make a list of the important things you want to do that will help you achieve your dreams . . .

Looking back at the list, decide which are the most important things to focus on right now and which are the things that you will focus on later.

Now think about things you might want to **stop doing** the things that **don't add value** to your life or that are holding you back from achieving your goals . . .

The Year Ahead . . .

In order to be on track in your life what would you like to achieve this year?

What would you most like to change about your life this year?

What concern, challenge or problem do you have that you'd like to solve?

What resolutions would you like to make for the year ahead?

Do you know why and how you want to do them?

What help might you ask for and from whom?

Think about the following areas and record what you want to **achieve** for each category over this **next year**:

Your health and fitness

Your family

Your friendships

Your work/study

Giving something to the community

.

Your finances

Your emotional well being/happiness

Fun and adventure

With this year plan in mind, what do you therefore need to **accomplish** over the next **three months?**

Your health and fitness

Your family

Your friendships

Your work/study

Giving something to the community

Your finances

Your emotional well being/happiness

Fun and adventure

What do you aim to do this month for each category

Your health and fitness

Your family

Your friendships

Your work/study

Giving something to the community

Your finances

Your emotional well being/happiness

Fun and adventure

What will you do this week?

Your health and fitness

Your family

Your friendships

Your work/study

Giving something to the community

Your finances

Your emotional well being/happiness

Fun and adventure

How are you going to **keep** yourself **on target**? Write down what you need to do to re-energise yourself each week . . .

What will you do and how would you like to be today?

One of the greatest discoveries a man makes, one of his great surprises, is to find he can do what he was afraid he couldn't do

Henry Ford

You're nearly done . . .

Now choose an age at which to imagine yourself in the future.

What might you be doing?

How might you be living?

What would you want to say to your future self, wish for yourself, and advise yourself?

Try writing a letter to your future self from you now.

Dear Future me

Good health, meaningful work, someone to love and be loved by and something to look forward to are the requirements for a great life.

Jonathan Heighway

You've worked hard on yourself.

Time to make sure you have something to look forward to.

What are you most looking forward to in the next few weeks?

Who are you most looking forward to spending time with?

How can you make that time special?

Where are you planning to go for your next holiday? What would you particularly like to do and with whom?

These extra pages are for you to make a note of any questions, thoughts or feelings that you may not have written elsewhere in the book . . .

And finally for the record . . .

What is your full name?

Your date of birth?

Your current address?

How tall are you?

What weight are you?

What are you wearing?

Describe the room that you are sitting in as you write this.
What can you see from the window?

Signature

Date book completed

If you liked the concept of this book, please tell your family and friends and look out for others in the current *from you to me* range:

Journals of a Lifetime

Dear Mum
Dear Dad
Dear Grandma
Dear Grandad
Dear Daughter
Dear Son
Dear Sister
Dear Brother
Dear Friend

Home Gift Journals

Cooking up Memories
Digging up Memories

Sport Gift Journals

Kicking off Memories

Leaving Gift Journals

These were the Days
Primary School Journals

Mother & Baby

Mum to Mum ... pass it on
Bump to first Birthday ... pregnancy & first year journal
Our Story ... for my Daughter
Our Story ... for my Son

Christmas Memories

Christmas Past, Christmas Present

Personalised

You can personalise the Journals of a Lifetime online at www.fromyoutome.com

All titles are available at gift and book shops or online at www.fromyoutome.com

Dear Future Me

from you to me®

First published in the UK by *from you to me*, October 2010
Copyright, *from you to me* limited 2010
Hackless House, Murhill, Bath, BA2 7FH
www.fromyoutome.com
E-mail: hello@fromyoutome.com

ISBN 978-1-907048-16-6

Cover design by so design consultants, Wick, Bristol, UK www.so-design.co.uk
Printed and bound in the UK by CPI Group (UK) Ltd, Croydon, CR0 4YY

This paper is manufactured from material sourced from forests certified according to strict environmental, social and economical standards.

All rights reserved. No part of this publication may be reproduced, stored in a retrieval system or transmitted in any form or by any means, electronic, mechanical, photocopying or otherwise circulated without the publisher's prior consent in any form of binding or cover other than that in which it is published and without a similar condition including this.